CLIMATE CHANGE COLORING BOOK

Coloring activities to explore climate data & research

Brian Foo

Edited by Allyza Lustig

Detailed documentation for all coloring activities can be found at:
coloringclimate.com/documentation/

ISBN 978-0-692-91311-6
First edition
Printed in the United States of America
Printed on 100% post consumer recycled, FSC certifed, chlorine free paper
Learn more book printing details at *coloringclimate.com/printing/*

Icons designed by Iconic, Rob Armes, Jonathan Li, and Oliviu Stoian
from *thenounproject.com*, Freepik from Flaticon

For Mom and Dad
who instilled in me a passion
for learning and coloring

This is not a coloring book for relaxation or a book for quick facts about climate change. The subject of climate change may evoke anxiety and urgency, the climate system is complex, and the act of coloring is slow. Although information about climate change is ultimately conveyed, this coloring book is especially suited to facilitate retention of facts and a reflection on the underlying issues relating to climate change. Lastly, this book was made using climate data and research from authoritative sources, but do not trust this book by itself. Ask questions, research the issues, check the sources, and verify the results. Take the appropriate actions.

Global carbon emissions from fossil fuels

Greenhouse gases (GHGs), including carbon dioxide, methane, and nitrous oxide, warm the Earth by absorbing energy and slowing the rate at which incoming solar radiation escapes to space. Essentially, GHGs act like a blanket insulating the planet. As human activities add more GHGs into the atmosphere, global land and ocean temperatures will rise.

Since 1751, around the start of the Industrial Revolution, just over 400 billion metric tons of carbon have been released to the atmosphere from the production and consumption of fossil fuels. Half of these fossil-fuel carbon emissions occurred since the mid-1980s. The latest available measurement of annual emissions are for the year 2014: according to the U.S. Department of Energy, approximately 9.9 billion metric tons of carbon were released globally, which represents an all-time high and a 0.8% increase over 2013 emissions.[1] In total, humans have increased the concentration of atmospheric carbon dioxide by more than a third since the Industrial Revolution began.[2]

The following page compares the **carbon emissions from fossil fuels in the years 1760, 1870, and 2014**. One dot represents one million metric tons of carbon emissions; **count how many dots you can color in for each year.**

[1] Boden, T.A., G. Marland, and R.J. Andres. 2016. *Global, Regional, and National Fossil-Fuel CO2 Emissions*. Carbon Dioxide Information Analysis Center, Oak Ridge National Laboratory, United States Department of Energy (DOE).

[2] *A blanket around the Earth*. Global Climate Change: Vital Signs of the Planet, National Aeronautics and Space Administration (NASA).

1760 (Industrial Revolution begins)

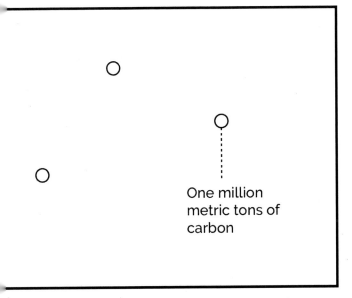

One million metric tons of carbon

1870 (Second Industrial Revolution begins)

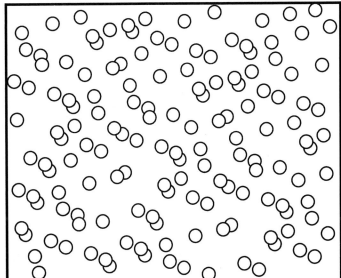

2014 (Latest measurement)

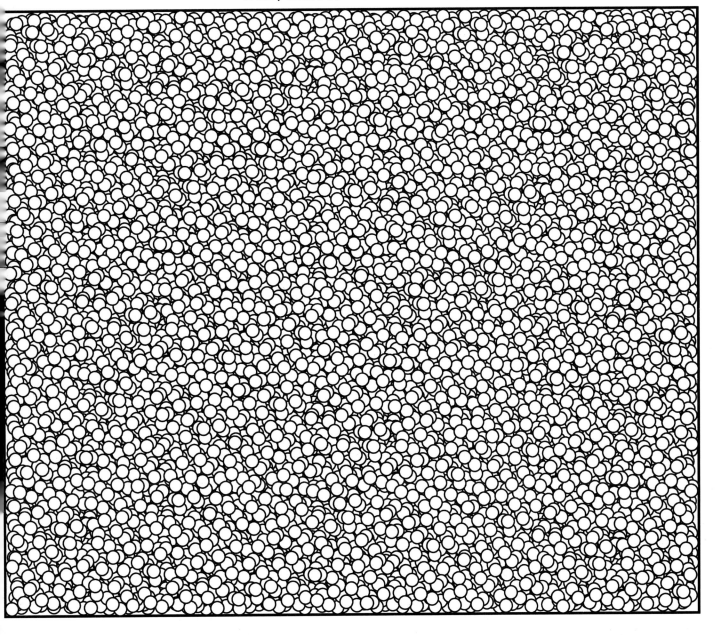

The hottest months on record

There are 137 years of reliable scientific measurements of global land and ocean temperature. Of that record, the 20 hottest years happened in the last 22 years. The hottest 5 years occurred in the last 7 years. The last 3 years were the warmest on record.[1] Of course, temperature estimates go back farther than 137 years. In fact, we can approximate the temperature on Earth thousands and millions of years ago. These estimations of the planet's past climate come from a number of sources, including tree rings, ice cores, and rock samples. This information is important because it allows us to understand the Earth's history and compare present day changes in temperature with variability in the past. Scientists tell us that in the last decade global average temperatures were higher than they have been for at least 75% of the last 11,300 years.[2]

Now let's zoom in a little. When was the warmest January on record, or February, or March? Understanding monthly or seasonal climate trends allows us to plan for impacts. If summers are getting hotter, we might expect to see more heat-related illness and mortality. If winters are getting warmer, agricultural pests will live through the season and possibly require a greater application of pesticides. These are just some of the many impacts of temperature increase on the seasonal scale.

The following page ranks the **hottest years of each month recorded since 1880,** which all occurred after 1990. **Color the months on the right according to the table below.** The darkest colors represent the hottest for each month on record. What patterns or trends do you notice?

Label	Color	For each month
1	Brown	*Hottest on record*
2	Violet	*2nd hottest on record*
3	Magenta	*3rd "*
4	Red	*4th "*
5	Pink	*5th "*
6	Peach	*6th "*
7	Orange	*7th "*
8	Gold	*8th "*
9	Yellow	*9th hottest on record*

[1] *Global Surface Temperature Anomalies.* National Oceanic and Atmospheric Administration (NOAA), National Centers for Environmental Information.

[2] *What's the Hottest Earth Has Been "Lately"?* National Oceanic and Atmospheric Administration (NOAA).

Year	Jan	Feb	Mar	Apr	May	Jun	Jul	Aug	Sep	Oct	Nov	Dec
1990			7									
1991												
1992												
1993												
1994												
1995		7										
1996												
1997											7	
1998	9	3		5	7	9	3	5				
1999		8										
2000												
2001										9		
2002	4	4	4						8	4		
2003	7											5
2004		5	8				8	9	6	6	6	
2005		8	9	8	8	8	8		9	8		8
2006												4
2007	2	9			6	9						
2008			6							9		9
2009					9	7	9	4	5			9
2010	5	6	3	2	4	4	4	8			3	
2011												
2012				7	5	5	6	6	4	5	7	
2013					6	6	7	7	7	7	2	6
2014	6		5	3	3	5	3	3	1	8	1	2
2015	3	2	2	4	2	2	2	2	1	1	1	1
2016	1	1	1	1	1	1	1	1	2	3	5	3

Where carbon emissions are the greatest

Human needs such as electricity, heating, and transportation often require the burning of fossil fuels. The U.S. accounts for about 15% of global fossil fuel emissions but just over 4% of the world population.

The map on the following page uses data provided by the National Oceanic and Atmospheric Administration (NOAA) and **shows where fossil fuel emissions are the greatest in the United States.[1] Use the table below to color each circle.** The darkest areas on the map indicate where urban infrastructure and residential heating and electricity use is the greatest. What do you notice about where these areas are located? Since fossil fuels release carbon dioxide into the atmosphere, a map of CO_2 emissions looks very similar to a map of population density.

Level	Color	2015 carbon emissions (metric tons per square kilometer)
1	White	Under 1
2	Yellow	1 to 10
3	Orange	10 to 100
4	Red	100 to 500
5	Brown	500 to 1000
6	Black	Over 1000

[1] *CarbonTracker CT2016.* National Oceanic and Atmospheric Administration (NOAA), Earth System Research Laboratory, Global Monitoring Division.

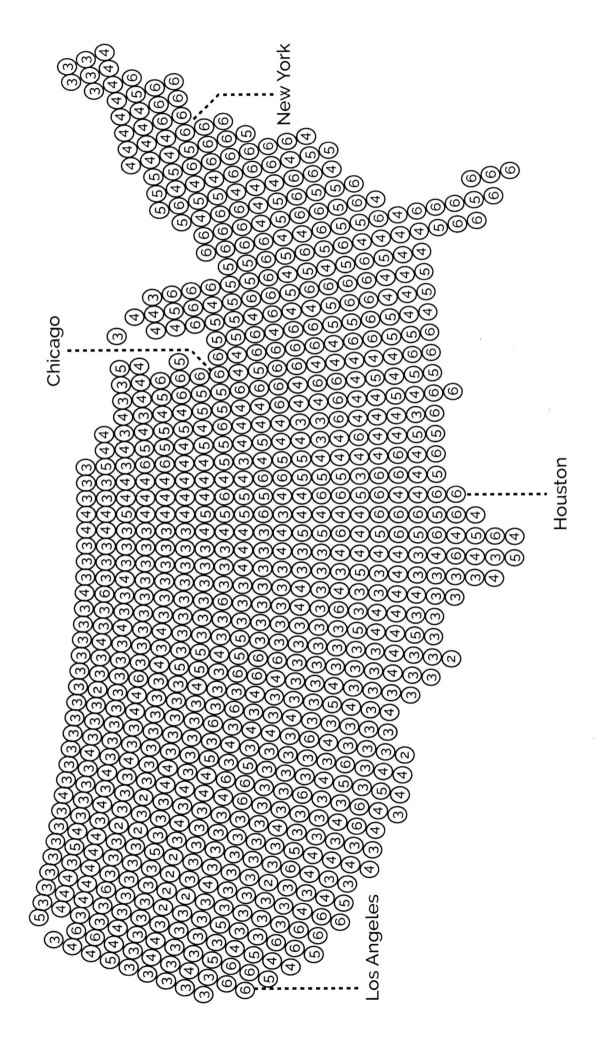

What drives global warming?

Climate forcings are different factors that affect the Earth's climate. These forcings drive or "force" the climate system to change. There are natural forcings and man-made forcings. Some natural forcings include volcanic eruptions, changes in the energy output of the sun, and changes in the Earth's orbit. But none of these factors significantly contributed to the global temperature increase of 1.9°F observed since 1880.[1] Only anthropogenic (i.e. man-made) forcings, in particular GHG emissions, can possibly explain the temperature increase observed in our recent history.

How do we know this? The activity on the right compares observed changes in global temperature from 1880 to 2005 with the three major natural forcings and one anthropogenic forcing. All data is generated by the National Aeronautics and Space Administration's Goddard Institute for Space Studies (NASA GISS).[2] Each trendline reflects the extent to which that particular forcing drove the Earth's climate to be warmer or cooler compared to the baseline 1880-1910 average.

For each climate forcing graph, **color the area above the baseline/under the trendline red**. This shows us when and how much the forcing drove warmer temperatures. **Color the area below the baseline/above the trendline blue**. This represents when and how much the forcing drove the cooler temperatures.

As you will see, the influence of orbital changes and solar temperature variation on the Earth's temperature over 125 years has been negligible. Stratospheric aerosols from volcanic eruptions can actually have a strong, cooling influence, but it is very short term. Meanwhile, greenhouse gases are shown to have the greatest sustained positive forcing on the Earth's climate system.

[1] *Global Surface Temperature Anomalies.* National Oceanic and Atmospheric Administration (NOAA), National Centers for Environmental Information

[2] *ModelE2 Climate Simulations.* National Aeronautics and Space Administration (NASA), Goddard Institute for Space Studies (GISS).

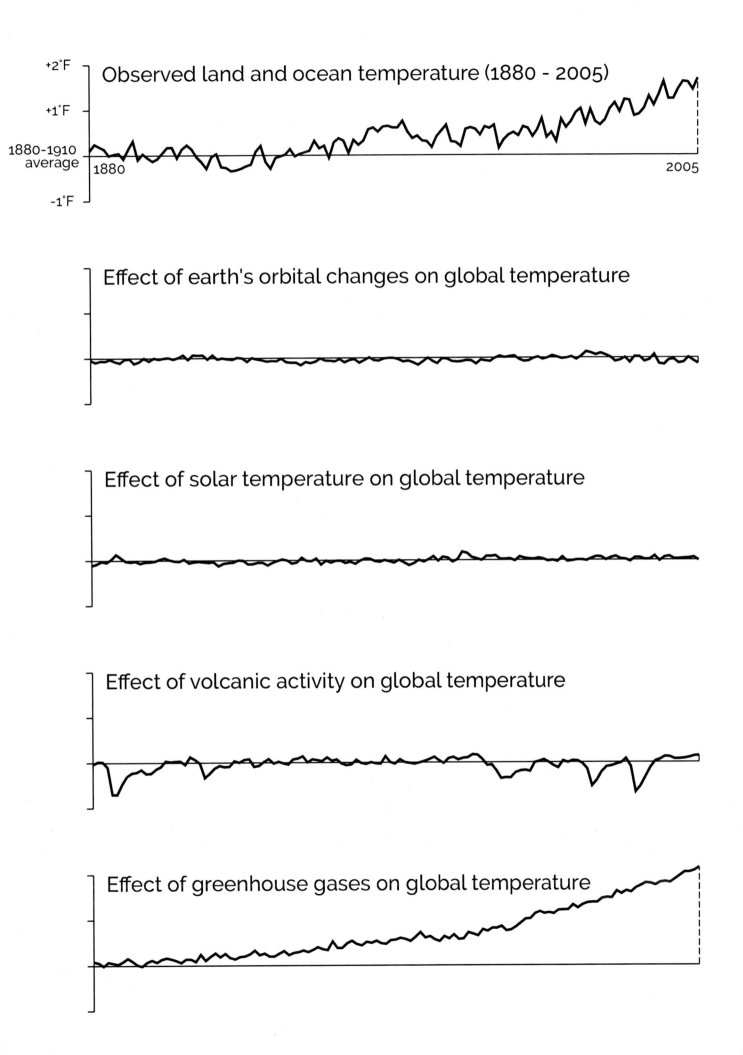

Global deforestation

Through the process of photosynthesis, trees remove carbon dioxide (CO_2) from the atmosphere, release oxygen (O_2), and store the carbon (C) for a long period of time. Therefore, forests are vital for mitigating the effects of climate change on the environment.

In contrast, forest clearing and the fires that accompany it generate one-tenth of all global warming emissions.[1] The Brazilian Amazon is the world's largest rainforest, and in 2015 nearly two million acres of forest were eliminated there in one year.[2] Deforestation in the Amazon and elsewhere has serious consequences for biodiversity. Many species have been wiped out due partially to aggressive land use practices. Although extinction is a natural process, it is happening much faster because of human activity.[3] In fact, scientists refer to the current wave species die-off as the 6th mass extinction -- what we are seeing now is similar to the end of the dinosaurs over 60 million years ago. Deforestation alone is not the only cause, and climate change also plays a role. According to one study, if greenhouse gas emissions continue to increase along their current trajectory, 16% of species will face extinction by the end of the century.[4]

According to the Food and Agriculture Organization of the United Nations (FAO), the world had 4,128 million hectares of forest in 1990. By 2015 this area had decreased to 3,999 million hectares of forest, a net loss of 129 million hectares over a 25 year period.[5] **This is equivalent to losing 20 football fields worth of forest every minute for 25 years.**

How fast can you color 20 football fields? Take out a stopwatch or timer and set it to one minute. See if you can color the 20 football fields on the right faster than we have been losing global forests.

[1] *Measuring the Role of Deforestation in Global Warming.* 2013. Union of Concerned Scientists.

[2] *PRODES estima 7.989 km2 de desmatamento por corte raso na Amazônia em 2016.* 2016. Brazil's National Institute for Space Research.

[3] Chaplin, F. S. III, Zavaleta, E. S., Eviner, V. T., Naylor, R. L., Vitousek, P. M., Reynolds, H. L., ... Díaz, S. (2000). *Consequences of changing biodiversity. Nature*, 405, 234-242. doi:10.1038/35012241

[4] *Climate Change Will Accelerate Earth's Sixth Mass Extinction.* 2015. Smithsonian Magazine.

[5] *Global Forest Resources Assessment 2015.* 2016. Food and Agriculture Organization of the United Nations (FAO).

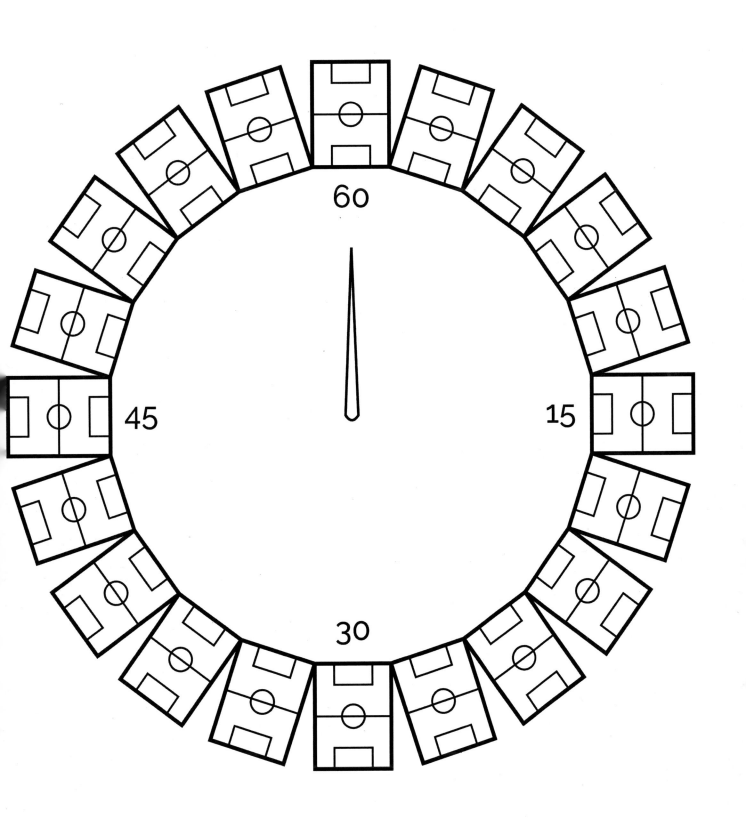

Air pollution in Beijing

When carbon-based fuels are burned, carbon dioxide and other pollutants are released into the atmosphere. Pollutants include particulate matter, which is a key component in the creation of smog. The effect of smog is complex; depending on the surrounding conditions, it can heat the Earth's climate by absorbing solar radiation.[1] When inhaled, these pollutants can also have serious negative effects on human health.

The Air Quality Index (AQI) is a standard for reporting daily air quality. It tells you how clean or polluted your air is and what associated health effects might be a concern for you. The reporting includes ground-level ozone and particulate matter, which are the two pollutants that pose the greatest threat to human health. The AQI is divided into the following categories.[2]

Level	Color	Air Quality
1	Green	Good
2	Yellow	Moderate
3	Orange	Unhealthy for Sensitive Groups
4	Red	Unhealthy
5	Purple	Very Unhealthy
6	Brown	Hazardous
7	Black	Beyond Index

On the right, there are **365 circles to represent each day in 2015** for Beijing, a city with a population of over 21 million people that is notorious for its air quality challenges. The circles are all labelled with the peak AQI level for that day.[3] **Fill in each circle with its associated color**. Note that some days have a level of 7, which represents measurements that exceed the most hazardous values supported by the index.

As you will see, air quality is the worst during the winter. More coal and other fossil fuels are burned during the cold winter months, and the AQI index is therefore higher. This is compounded by the tendency for low temperatures to exacerbate smog: warm air rises and settles above a layer of cooler, denser, smog-ridden air, trapping it at the Earth's surface.[4]

[1] *Aerosols: Tiny Particles, Big Impact.* National Aeronautics and Space Administration (NASA)

[2] *Air Quality Index.* United States Environmental Protection Agency (EPA).

[3] *Beijing Historical Data 2015.* United States Embassy Beijing Air Quality Monitor. United States Department of State.

[4] *Smog and Haze in Northern China.* 2016. Earth Observatory, National Aeronautics and Space Administration (NASA).

Warming and rising seas

Global sea level has been rising over the past century, and the rate has increased in recent decades to about one-eighth of an inch per year. There are two major causes of global sea level rise (SLR). The first is thermal expansion, which is caused by ocean warming. The oceans absorb more than 90 percent of the atmospheric heat associated with GHG emissions, and water expands as it warms.[1] The second cause of SLR is increased melting of glaciers and ice sheets. Water that was previously held in a solid state melts into the ocean and thus the sea level rises.

Higher sea levels mean that storm surge will push farther inland than it did in the past. SLR also means that certain coastal communities and infrastructure will be regularly flooded by new high tide levels, and eventually will be permanently inundated.

The following page illustrates **the relationship between ocean warming**[2] **and sea level rise**[3] between 1995 to 2015. Each curving horizontal line reflects the change in mean sea level every five years starting in 1995. **Color the areas under each line according to the table below.** This will show the change in ocean temperature relative to the 20th century average for each month of that year. Darker colors represent relatively warmer seas.

Label	Color	Change from 20th century average temperature (°F)
W	White	+ 0°F
Y	Yellow	
O	Orange	
R	Red	
V	Violet	
B	Brown	+ 1.5°F

[1] *Is sea level rising?* National Oceanic and Atmospheric Administration (NOAA), National Ocean Service.

[2] *Global Surface Temperature Anomalies.* National Oceanic and Atmospheric Administration (NOAA), National Centers for Environmental Information

[3] *Global sea level time series.* National Oceanic and Atmospheric Administration (NOAA), Laboratory for Satellite Altimetry.

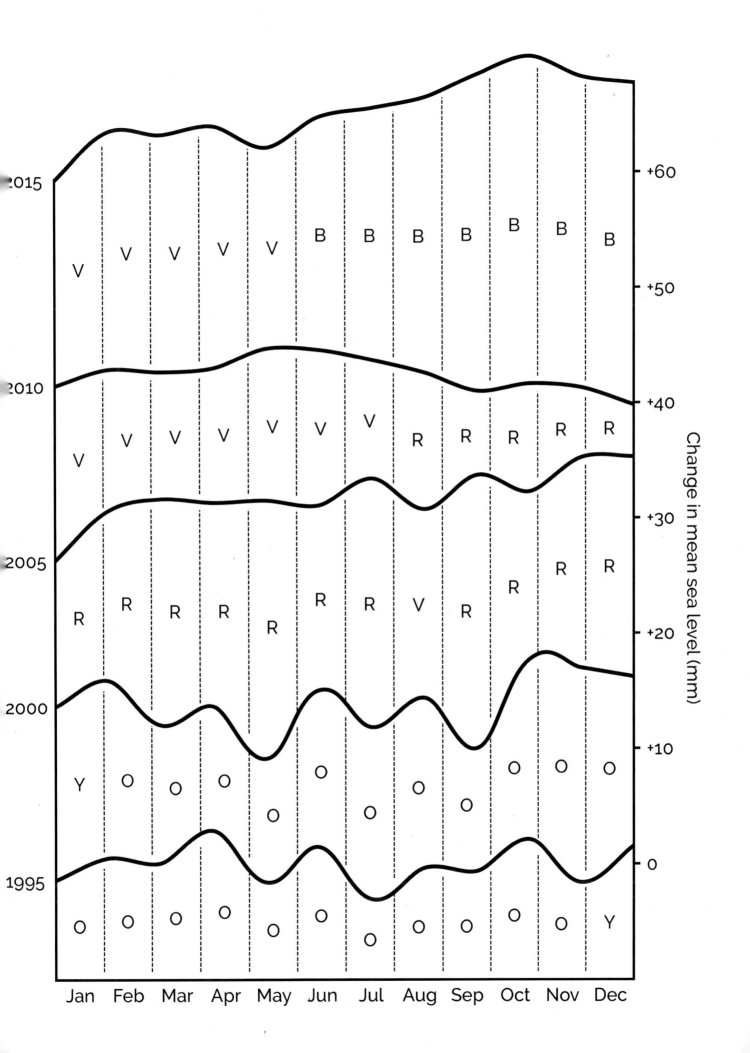

Shrinking Arctic sea ice

Sea ice, or frozen ocean water, covers part of the Arctic Ocean year-round. Even though sea ice occurs primarily in the polar regions, it influences our global climate. Sea ice has a bright surface, so much of the sunlight that strikes it is reflected back into space, keeping polar regions relatively cool. If gradually warming temperatures melt sea ice over time, fewer bright surfaces will be there to reflect sunlight back into space. In fact, the darker surfaces beneath the ice will absorb more solar energy, and temperatures will rise further. This positive feedback loop continues a cycle of warming and melting.

The area covered by sea ice is typically smallest in September after the summer melting season. Sea ice is dramatically altered by climate change since ice easily changes between solid and liquid states in response to relatively minor changes in temperature. September Arctic sea ice is now declining at a rate of 13.3 percent per decade, relative to the 1981 to 2010 average.

On the following page, the solid line shows the Arctic sea ice extent (that is, the area with at least 15% ice concentration) in September 2016. The dotted line shows the Arctic sea ice extent in September 1996, 20 years earlier.[1] **Color in the striped area between these two lines**. This area represents a **difference of 3.15 million square kilometers** of sea ice, about the size of India.

[1] Fetterer, F., K. Knowles, W. Meier, and M. Savoie. 2016. *Sea Ice Index, Version 2*. National Snow and Ice Data Center (NSIDC).

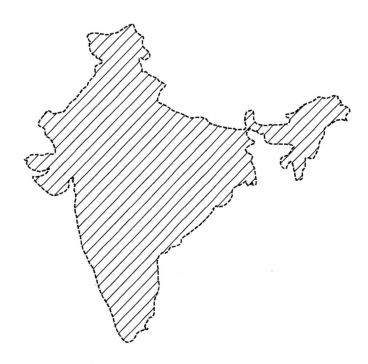

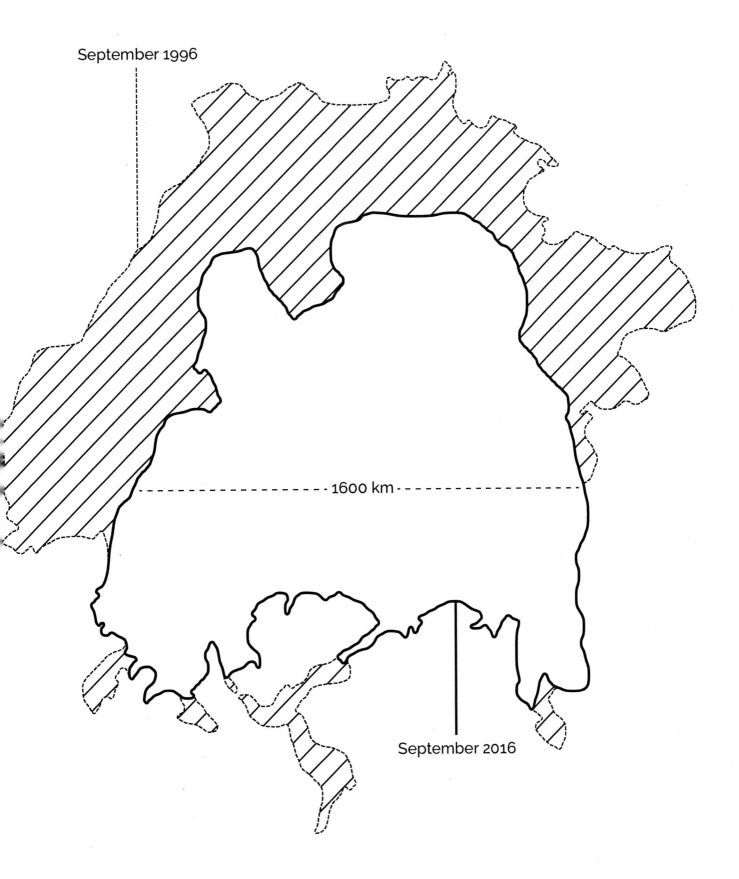

September 1996

1600 km

September 2016

Sea level scenarios

Even if we stop burning fossil fuels today, temperatures and sea levels will continue to rise for hundreds of years because carbon pollution persists in the atmosphere for a long period of time. This means that certain levels of global carbon emissions can "lock in" certain sea levels in the future.

Global temperature increase of 2 °C (3.6 °F) is a long-standing international target and corresponds to what many would consider a successful global effort to control greenhouse gas emissions. It also corresponds to 4.7 meters (15.4 feet) of global SLR . Warming of 4 °C (7.2 °F) is closer to our current path where current emissions rates continue. That corresponds to 8.9 m (29.2 ft) of global SLR.[1]

SLR presents a daunting challenge for coastal managers and planners. How much SLR should we expect and when? Will communities have to retreat from the shoreline? Where and when should we defend the coast? Planning for lower levels of sea level rise makes sense for the short term, but the uncertainty means that we must implement flexible defense methods that can be adjusted in the future.

The maps of Manhattan on the following page show scientific projections of what post-2100 Manhattan will look like depending on the path we take for reducing or escalating carbon emissions. The area outlined in dotted lines is land at risk of SLR inundation. The 2 °C scenario requires that people worldwide make sustainable choices. This involves a wide range of actions, including (but not limited to) using climate-smart energy technologies (e.g. wind and solar), cutting back on deforestation, and changing consumer behavior. The 4°C scenario assumes humans will continue to accelerate the rate at which we emit carbon dioxide, which is consistent with a global economy that continues to rely mainly on fossil fuels.[2]

Color the the water blue and the land that will be lost red. In the two scenarios, somewhere between centuries and millennia from now, the areas in red are permanently underwater, including most of lower Manhattan, East Harlem, and Inwood. Other major coastal cities around the country and the world such as Miami, New Orleans, Boston, Mumbai, and Shanghai will experience similar transformations.

[1] Strauss, Kulp, Levermann 2015. *Carbon choices determine US cities committed to futures below sea level.* Proceedings of the National Academy of Sciences.

[2] Strauss, Kulp, Levermann, Climate Central. *Surging Seas, Mapping Choices.*

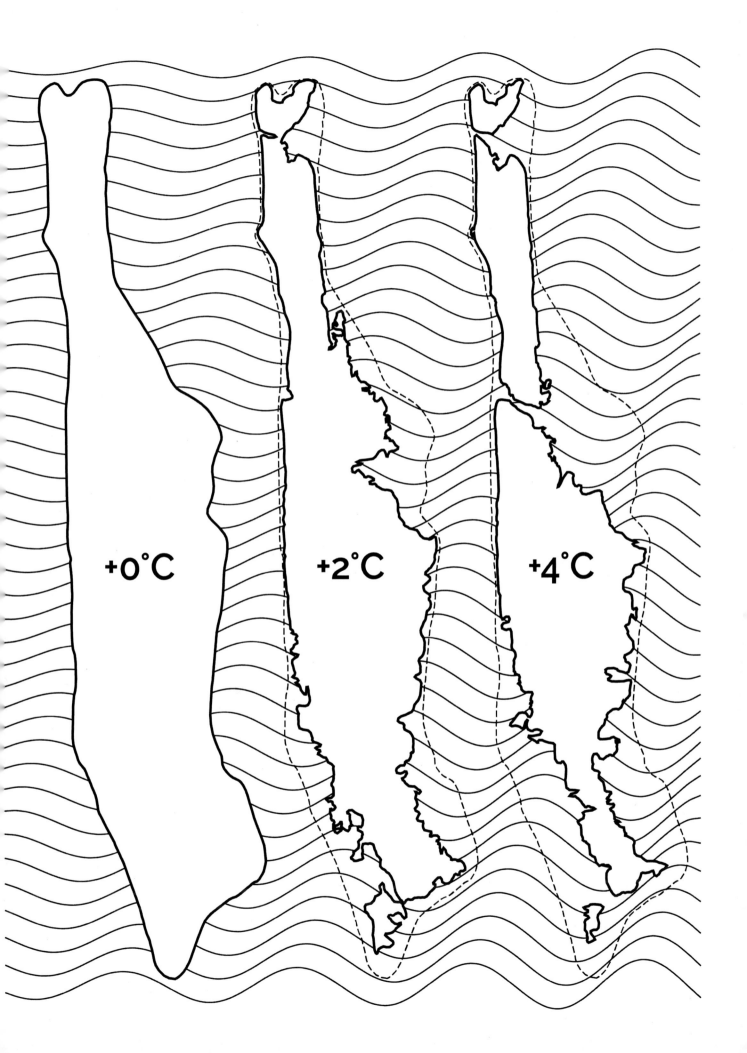

Rising tides and coastal flooding

Sea level rise around the globe is not uniform. Ocean currents and wind patterns cause water buildups in some areas. Ocean temperatures vary and warmer areas have higher levels because water expands as it warms. As ice sheets melt, the the land that had previously been weighed down begins to lift. Meanwhile, other land sinks in response. For example, Canada rises about four inches per decade while the eastern coast of the U.S. sinks at a rate of about 0.3 inches each year. That is more than half the rate of current global sea level rise.[1] On a very local level, water pumping may result in land subsidence that lowers the land relative to the ocean. Because of these factors, the impact of sea level rise varies around the globe.

In the U.S., the East and Gulf coasts are particularly prone to the effects of sea level rise. Such effects are already being observed through flooding caused by nothing more than high tides. Known as "sunny day" flooding, this new reality is forcing cities to spend millions repairing roads, drains, and homes, and investing in raised streets, seawalls, and pumps.

The following page shows three coastal cities that have seen a sharp jump in tidal flooding in recent years. **To illustrate the relationship between sea level rise[2] and tidal flooding[3], color the bars according to the table below**. Darker colors represent more days of tidal flooding.

Label	Color	Days of tidal flooding that year
W	White	5 or less
Y	Yellow	6 to 10
O	Orange	11 to 20
R	Red	21 to 40
B	Brown	41 to 60
K	Black	Over 60

[1] *Melting Glaciers Are Wreaking Havoc on Earth's Crust.* Smithsonian Magazine. 2016.

[2] *Sea Level Trends.* National Oceanic and Atmospheric Administration (NOAA), The Center for Operational Oceanographic Products and Services (CO-OPS).

[3] *Inundation Analysis Tool.* National Oceanic and Atmospheric Administration (NOAA), The Center for Operational Oceanographic Products and Services (CO-OPS).

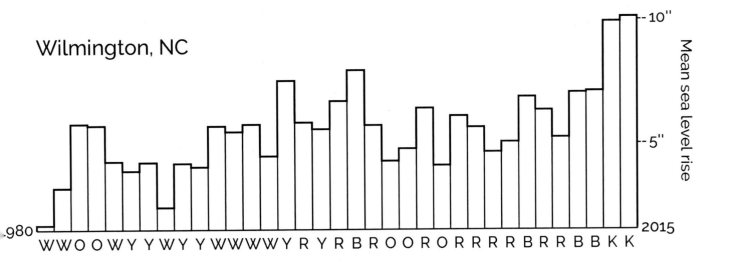

Wilmington, NC

Mean sea level rise

−10"

−5"

980 ... 2015

W W O O W Y Y W Y Y W W W W W Y R Y R B R O O R O R R R R B R R R B B K K

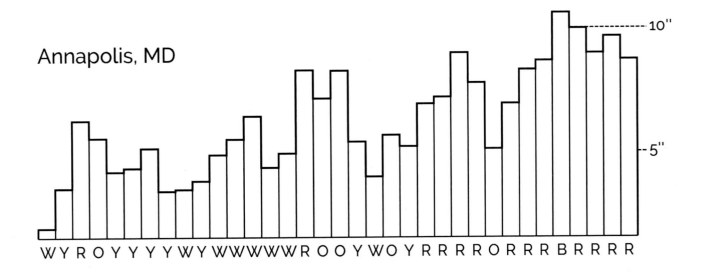

Annapolis, MD

−10"

−5"

W Y R O Y Y Y Y W Y W W W W W W R O O Y W O Y R R R R O R R R B R R R R

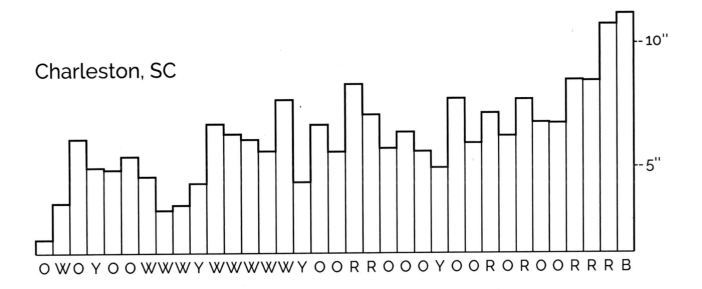

Charleston, SC

−10"

−5"

O W O Y O O W W W Y W W W W W W Y O O R R O O O Y O O R O R O O R R R B

Typhoons and the Philippines

Typhoons are storms that occur in the western Pacific Ocean that form over large bodies of relatively warm water. Because of the complexity of storm systems and the many factors affecting their formation and strength, scientists have not yet reached consensus on climate change's direct contributions to typhoon activity. However, scientists do increasingly agree that these storms will become more intense as oceans warm.[1] This is because typhoons, hurricanes, and all tropical storms draw their vast energy from the warmth of the sea.

The Philippines is a country made up of over 7,000 islands located in the western Pacific Ocean and surrounded by naturally warm waters. It is also situated in the Earth's most active typhoon region. Therefore, if climate change has an effect on typhoon intensity, the Philippines would likely feel the effects early and considerably. There is already evidence that the intensity of typhoons have been increasing over the past few decades in the Philippines.[2]

The following page displays the **ten deadliest typhoons that hit the Philippines in chronological order since 1950**. Five of the ten deadliest typhoons occurred after 2006 over a period of just seven years, killing over 13,000 people and displacing millions. **The size of each circle represents the number of dead or missing** as a direct result of each storm. The latest and deadliest storm on record in the Philippines is Typhoon Haiyan (locally known as Yolanda), which brought winds at nearly 200 miles per hour, killed 6,300 people, and left another 1,061 missing or presumed dead.[3]

[1] *Global Warming and Hurricanes.* National Oceanic and Atmospheric Administration (NOAA), Geophysical Fluid Dynamics Laboratory (GFDL).

[2] Mei et al. *Northwestern Pacific typhoon intensity controlled by changes in ocean temperatures.* 2015. Science Advances, Vol. 1, no. 4.

[3] *Final Report re Effects of Typhoon "Yolanda" (Haiyan).* 2013. National Disaster Risk Reduction and Management Council, Republic of the Philippines (NDRRMC).

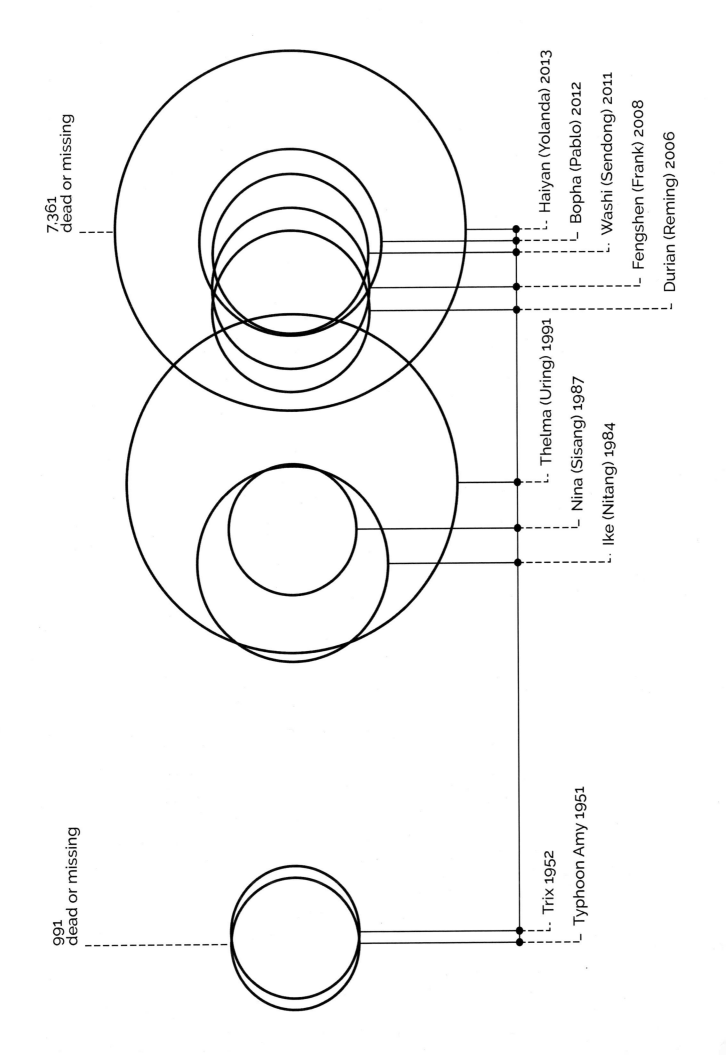

Coral bleaching of the Great Barrier Reef

Climate change also has serious implications for marine ecosystems. The rising concentration of carbon dioxide in the atmosphere increases the absorption of carbon dioxide by the ocean, which increases ocean acidity. Warmer oceans also hold less oxygen, especially in the deep ocean. Both of these phenomenon make survival harder for marine life.

Warming ocean temperatures also increase the risk of coral bleaching, which can lead to the loss of critical habitat for marine species. Coral reefs hold some of the richest and most diverse life in the world's oceans. They also supply hundreds of millions of people with food and generate billions of dollars in income through tourism each year. Corals thrive in warm waters, but are very sensitive to extra heat, which causes them to expel the algae living inside them and turn completely white. This is called coral bleaching. If corals are bleached too frequently without time to recover, they become more likely to die by starvation or disease.

The Great Barrier Reef, located in the Coral Sea off the coast of Australia, is the world's largest coral reef system and is composed of over 2,900 individual reefs. Warming oceans caused by climate change have contributed to three global mass bleaching events since 1998. The latest in 2016 is the longest and worst global coral bleaching event in history. **Scientists have confirmed the largest die-off of corals ever recorded on Australia's Great Barrier Reef.**[1]

Australia's Great Barrier Reef Marine Park Authority surveyed 873 individual reefs.[2] **Color the following page according to the table below** which illustrates their findings.

[1] *Life and death after Great Barrier Reef bleaching.* 2016. ARC Centre of Excellence for Coral Reef Studies.

[2] *Interim report: 2016 coral bleaching event on the Great Barrier Reef.* 2016. Great Barrier Reef Marine Park Authority, Australian Government.

Label	Color	Level of coral bleaching
0	Green	No bleaching
1	Yellow	Minor bleaching
2	Orange	Moderate bleaching
3	Red	Severe bleaching

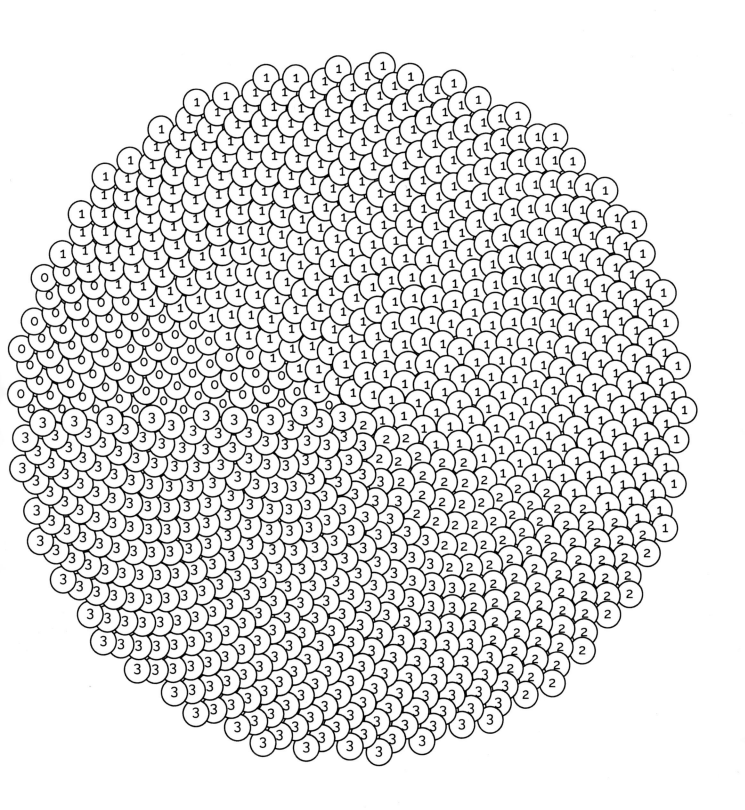

Equivalence[1]

The carbon emissions of **one car** can be removed from the atmosphere by **4 acres** of North American pine forest.

[1] *Greenhouse Gases Equivalencies Calculator - Calculations and References*. United States Environmental Protection Agency (EPA).

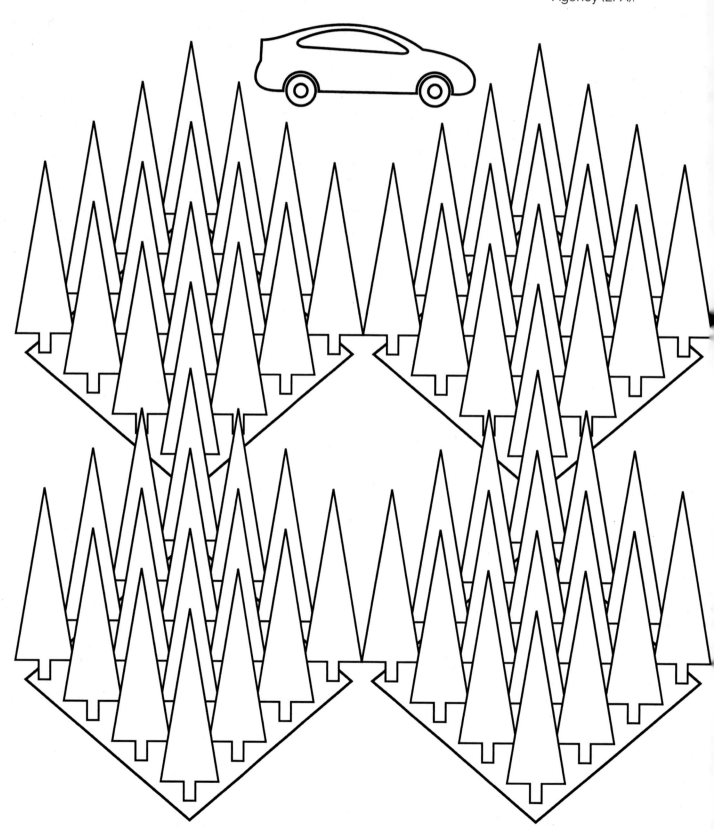

Equivalence (continued)

Taking **one car** off the road for a year is equivalent to planting **121 urban tree seedlings** and growing them for 10 years.

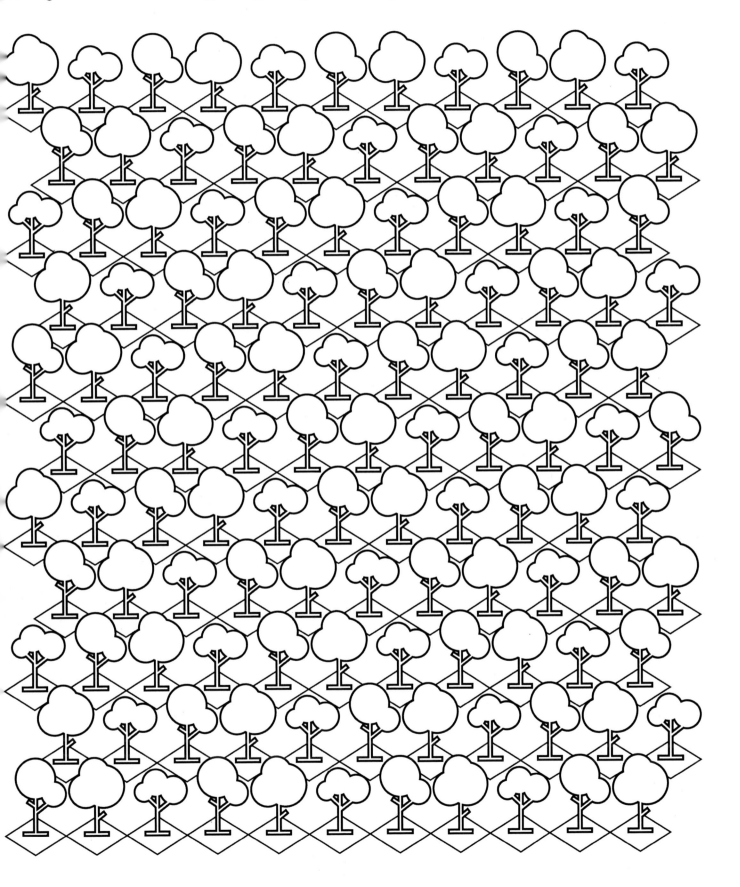

Equivalence (continued)

Recycling one garbage truck of waste instead of adding it to a landfill is equivalent to taking **5 cars** off the road for one year.

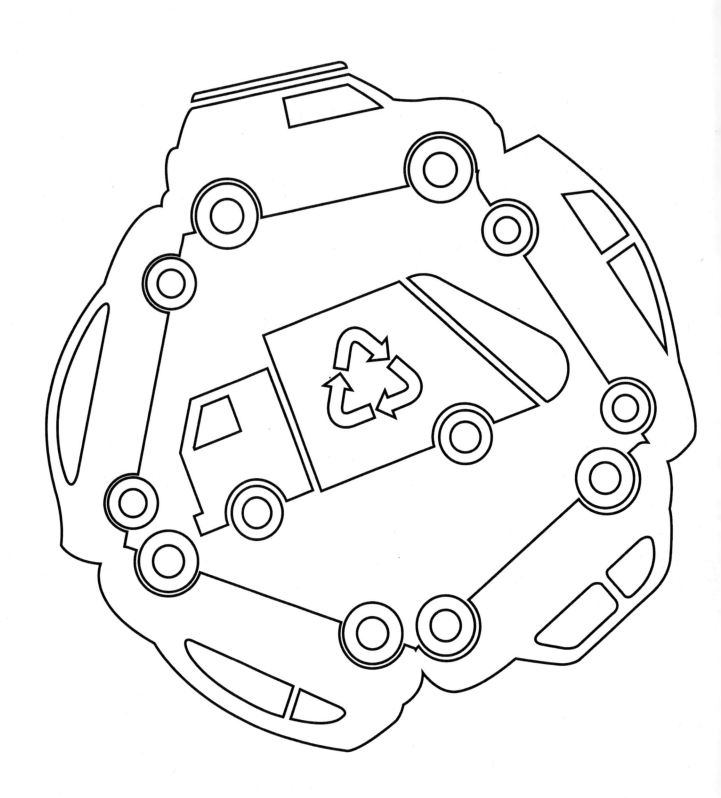

Equivalence (continued)

One wind turbine offsets the carbon emissions of **837 cars** per year.

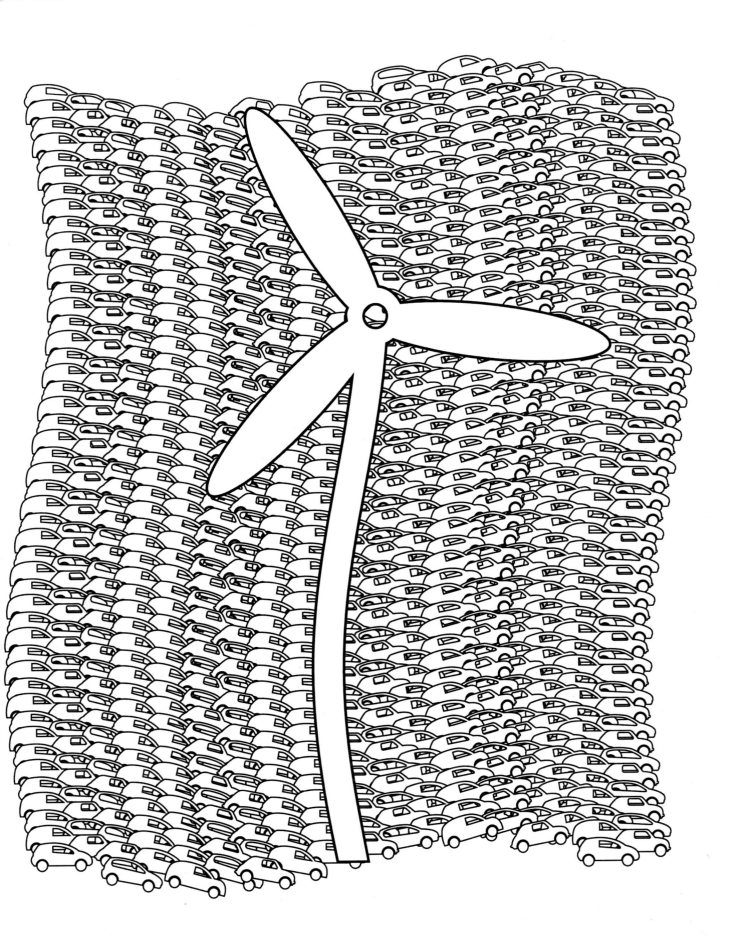

Scientific consensus

What percentage of scientists have concluded that climate change is caused by human activity?[1] **Color the YES arrows GREEN**, representing scientists who have concluded that climate change is caused by human activity. **Color NO arrows RED** for those who do not agree.

[1] Cook *et al.* *Consensus on consensus: a synthesis of consensus estimates on human-caused global warming.* 2016. Environmental Research Letters, 11.

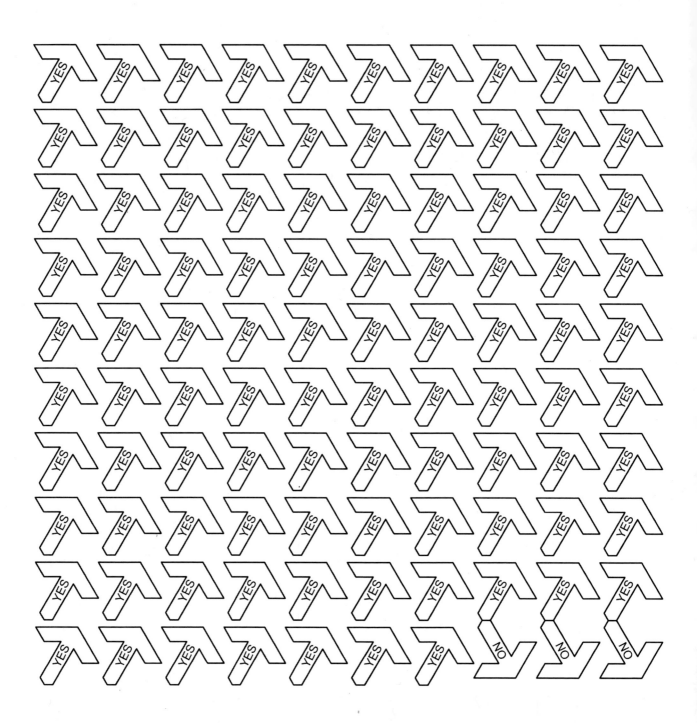

Public perception

What percentage of Americans believe that climate change is caused by human activity?[1] **Color the YES arrows GREEN,** representing individuals who believe that climate change is caused by human activity. **Color NO arrows RED,** for those who do not agree.

[1] Survey conducted May 10-June 6, 2016. *The Politics of Climate.* Pew Research Center.

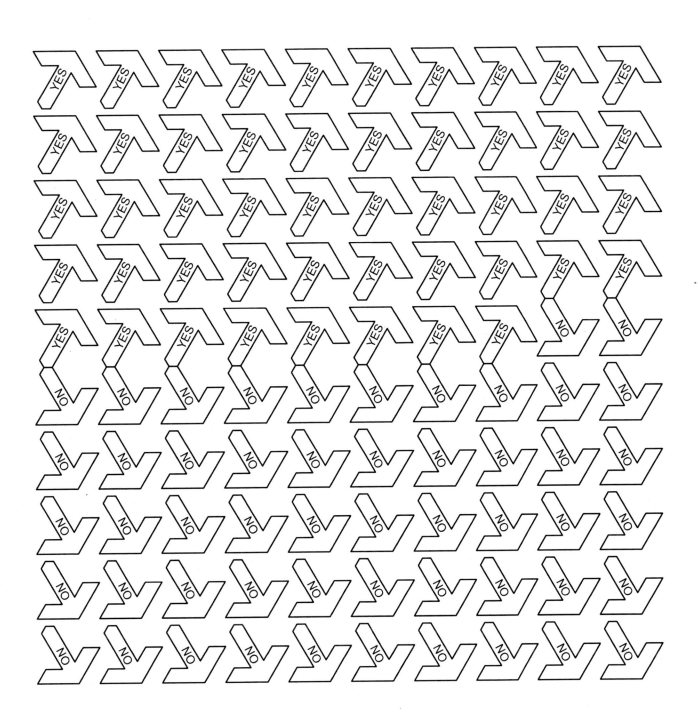

Renewable energy potential

According to the United States Department of Energy, the U.S. consumed over 97 quadrillion BTUs of energy in 2016[1], equivalent to the amount of energy consumed by 1.5 billion cars driven for one year.[2] However, only about 10 percent of the country's energy demand was met with renewable energy, which includes hydroelectric, geothermal, solar, wind, and biomass. The majority of the energy consumed in the U.S. comes from fossil fuels.

The U.S. Department of Energy has also estimated the country's potential energy production from renewable energy technologies. These estimates consider resource availability, physical potential of resources, available technology, land limitations, and land-use constraints, but do not consider economic or market factors. Their calculations find that **renewable energy sources can potentially provide over 14 times the energy we currently consume.** The state of Texas alone could generate the whole country's energy needs with just solar power technology.[3] Separate research reveals that the market may be evolving to meet the energy potential: Solar job opportunities are on the rise and are increasing 12 times faster than the rest of the U.S. economy. Wind energy jobs have seen a 32% increase since 2015.[4] Researchers estimate that investment in renewable energy results in approximately three times more jobs than similar investment in fossil fuels.[5]

Color the circles on the following page according to the table below.

Color	United States in 2016	
Yellow	*Actual* energy generated using renewable energy technologies	
Blue	*Actual* energy consumed	
Green	*Potential* energy generated using renewable energy technologies	

[1] Primary energy consumption estimates by source, *Annual Energy Review. 2016.* Energy Information Administration (EIA).

[2] *Greenhouse Gases Equivalencies Calculator - Calculations and References.* United States Environmental Protection Agency (EPA).

[3] Lopez, A., B. Roberts, D. Heimiller, N. Blair, G. Porro. 2012. *U.S. Renewable Energy Technical Potentials. A GIS-Based Analysis.* National Renewable Energy Laboratory (NREL).

[4] *Now Hiring: The Growth of America's Green and Sustainable Jobs.* 2017. Environmental Defense Fund.

[5] Garrett-Peltier, H. 2016. *Green versus brown: Comparing the employment impacts of energy efficiency, renewable energy, and fossil fuels using an input-output model.* University of Massachusetts Amherst.

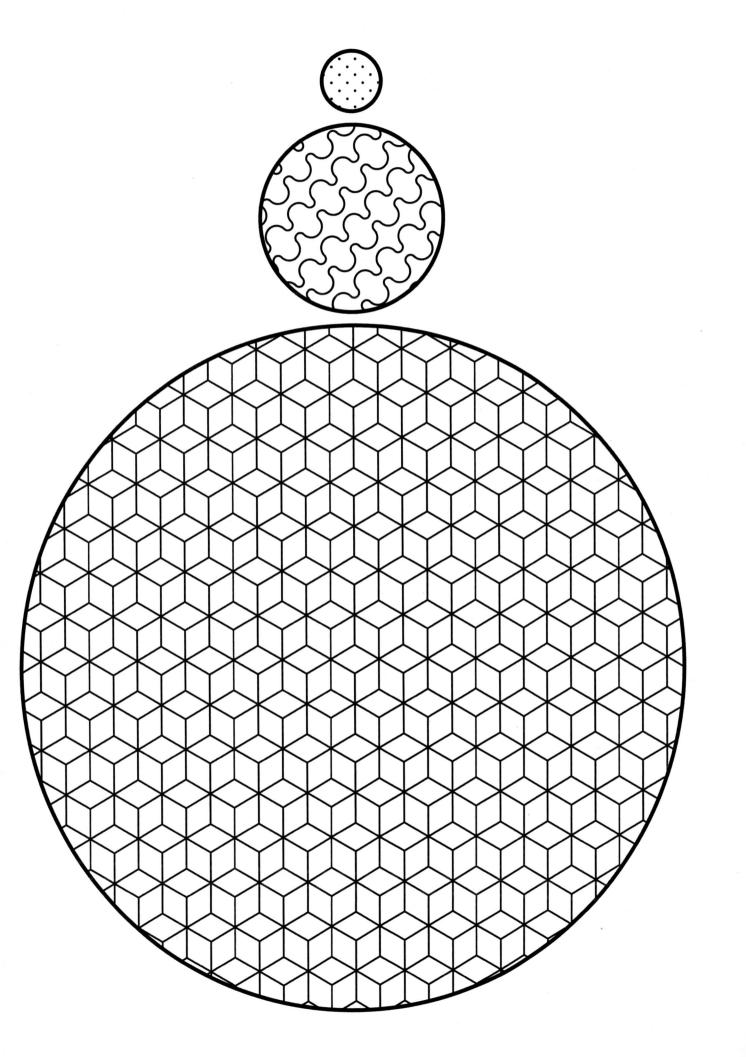

Carbon dioxide emissions by transport type

Consider a trip from Boston to New York, a 215 mile journey by road, 190 miles by plane. In terms of minimal direct CO_2 emissions, biking is the best way to get around, although not always feasible. A passenger who travels by car is responsible for two times more CO_2 emissions than a passenger who travels by bus. Similarly, a passenger who travels by plane is responsible for 20 times more CO_2 emissions than a passenger who travels by train.

The following page shows the approximate direct carbon emissions per passenger of seven different forms of transportation on a trip from Boston to New York.[1] **Color each cell, which represents one kilogram of direct CO_2 emissions per passenger, according to the table below**. The colors will highlight the differences between the carbon emissions of each transport type.

[1] *Focusing on environmental pressures from long-distance transport.* European Environment Agency, 2014.

Level	Color
1	Yellow
2	Orange
3	Red
4	Purple
5	Brown
6	Black

All measurements have been estimated with an average number of passengers per vehicle. For example, 88 passengers for a plane, 156 passengers for a train, 13 passengers for a bus, 4 passengers for a carpool, and 1.5 passengers for a car. The addition of more passengers results in more fuel consumption--and hence CO_2 emissions--as the vehicle becomes heavier, but the CO_2 emissions per passenger becomes lower.

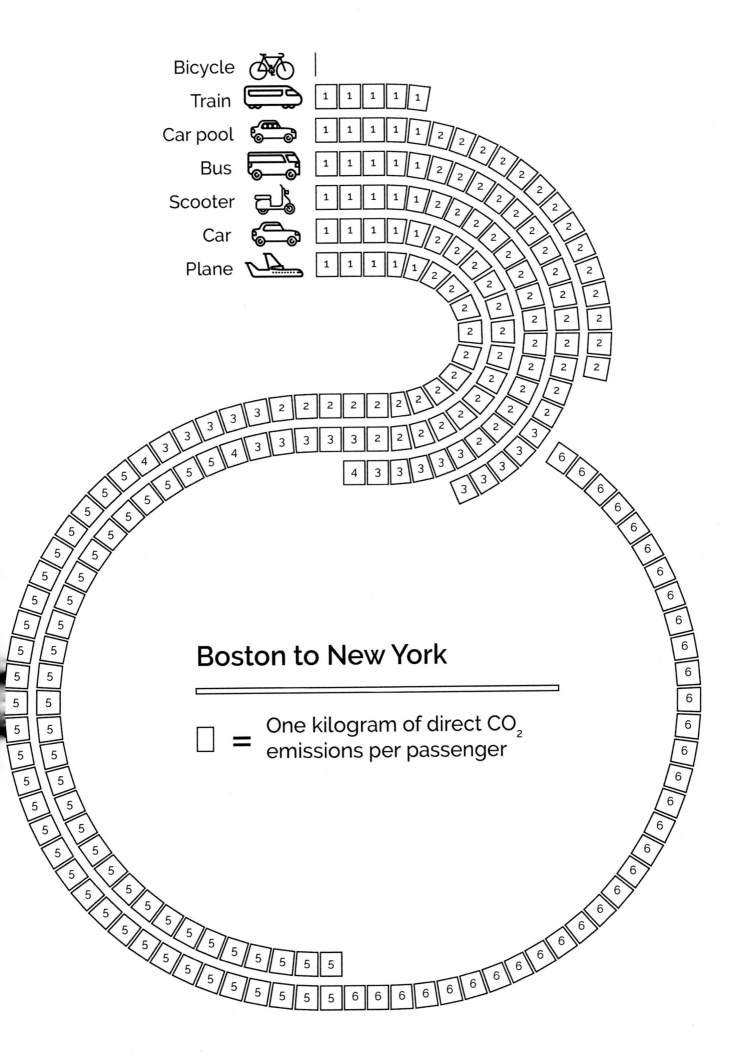

Boston to New York

□ = One kilogram of direct CO_2 emissions per passenger

Light bulb census

Compared to traditional incandescent light bulbs, energy-efficient light bulbs such as compact fluorescent lamps (CFLs) and light emitting diodes (LEDs) typically use about 75 to 80 percent less energy and can last 10 to 25 times longer.[1] For each incandescent light bulb switched to an energy-efficient one, there will be less carbon emissions and less money spent on energy and new light bulbs. LED bulbs are even more efficient than CFLs.

For each incandescent light bulb that you replace with an LED light bulb, you can save $18 per year. The carbon emission reductions of a single light bulb replacement is equivalent to planting one urban tree seedling and letting it grow for ten years.[2] Replacing a CFL with an LED saves you $1 -- not as drastic, but notable in mass.

How much can your household save per year? Go around your home and color the following page according to the light bulbs you find. Once you found all the light bulbs, **calculate your annual savings if you switch all light bulbs to LED light bulbs.**

[1] *How Energy-Efficient Light Bulbs Compare with Traditional Incandescents.* United States Department of Energy (DOE), Office of Energy Efficiency & Renewable Energy.

[2] *Greenhouse Gases Equivalencies Calculator - Calculations and References.* United States Environmental Protection Agency (EPA).

Incandescent Bulbs   Compact Fluorescent Bulbs

× $18
_____

[   ]   **+**   [   ]   **=**   [   ]

Annual savings if bulbs are
replaced with LED bulbs

× $1
_____

This book was made possible by **829 backers** on Kickstarter

Brian Foo is an artist and computer scientist based in New York City. He is a data visualization artist at the American Museum of Natural History working on public exhibits related to climate change. His work has been featured on NPR, Information is Beautiful Awards, The Washington Post, The Atlantic, and The New York Times.

brianfoo.com

Allyza Lustig is a climate change adaptation specialist and science communicator living in New York City. She has worn various hats within NOAA, Columbia University's Earth Institute, and the Urban Ecology and Design Laboratory at Yale University.